Exe in
with an Exeter

How to use this book

This booklet is a source of information and reference concerning the long history of flooding along the course of the River Exe but the authors assume that an understanding of this material is considerably enhanced by linking it to an interactive walk through riverside Exeter.

Directions for reaching the first location on the walk (the radial gates) are given on page 2. There follows an introduction describing the long history of flooding along the River Exe and explaining some reasons for such floods. It is anticipated that, on a warm sunny day, the introduction can be read as you lean comfortably against the riverside wall near the radial gates but, if the weather is inclement, you may prefer to read the introduction before walking to this location and picking up the commentary on page 14. Directions for following the walk are in **bold print**, together with a straightforward commentary. More detailed points of interest are displayed in the green-tinted boxes and may be referred to as desired.

Starting the walk

L eaving Exeter St David's railway station, turn left and begin by walking northwards, passing 'The Artful Dodger' and 'The Red Cow' on your right (see map below). Then turn left, westwards, along Station Road, over the level-crossing. Walk on the right-hand side of Station Road so that you can look upstream, northwards. Immediately after crossing the main channel of the River Exe, and before you cross a side channel by a second bridge, there is an access gate to the riverbank on your right. Although a notice prohibits vehicles, you are permitted to walk here. Pass through the gate and follow the short stretch of surfaced track northwards towards some concrete structures. At the end of the track, with the concrete structures on your right and the main channel of the Exe ahead to the north, find a convenient spot to read the introductory pages which follow. If you have already read the introduction then you may wish to turn to page 14 immediately.

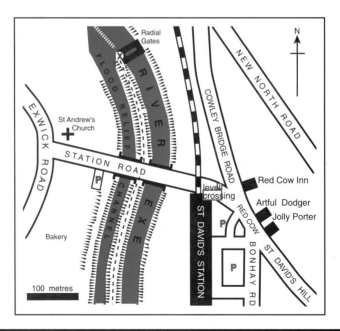

Map: Walking to the first location; the Exwick radial gates.

2

Why does the Exe flood?

Looking upstream (northwards) the elements which are important for understanding why rivers flood can be recognised. The river has cut itself a channel within which its waters can be accommodated most of the time. However, once every year or so, when the river is transporting an exceptional volume of water, it will overtop its banks and spread over the extensive flat land (here to the right of the river channel). Water flowing over this flat land will be shallow and slow-moving and so the fine sediments (silts and clays) being carried by the river will be deposited. Such an area is called the floodplain and is created by the river over a very long period.

Floodplains are a natural feature of most rivers over some part of their course. It is important as it provides the greater capacity the river needs at times when the river is exceptionally full. Some rivers may have very wide floodplains but most in South-West England are relatively narrow. Over time, the precise position of the river channel may vary within the floodplain. This tendency for river channels to change position is called meandering. Today the channel is to the left of the floodplain but, if left alone, in time it will move to some other position. Flooding is a natural feature of most rivers but it can be made worse.

Why the floods got worse

As Exeter grew, the floods got worse. One way in which flooding may be made worse is when building takes place on the floodplain. As Exeter has grown, the flat land of the floodplain was considered an attractive area for development. To protect these houses against regular winter inundations, parts of the floodplain have been raised and/or flood banks have been erected to keep away river waters. To the right-hand side of the floodplain you can see an example of a flood barrier protecting the railway lines. Constructing barriers or raising land reduces the area into which flood waters can then spread. Instead, the water has to pass downstream, there, raising river levels and possibly causing inundation at a location downstream.

Bridges can make floods worse. When a bridge is constructed across a river its arches and supports may slow down the river and reduce the volume of water which can pass under the bridge. Thus at times of a large flow, the river may overtop its banks immediately upstream of the bridge, causing an inundation at a place where floods were previously uncommon. A bridge may also cause blockages should debris, such as branches or even whole trees, become trapped against the bridge supports.

Making it worse downstream

Inevitably, extensive construction on one part of a floodplain - whether raised land, buildings, embanked roads or railway lines - results in worse floods downstream. It is not surprising that, over many centuries, the encroachment of the northern parts of the City of Exeter onto the floodplain has accentuated the flood problem further downstream in the southern parts of the city. Similarly, the riverside growth of villages and towns in the upper parts of the Exe Valley have added to the flood problems of Exeter.

Map: The drainage basin of the River Exe.

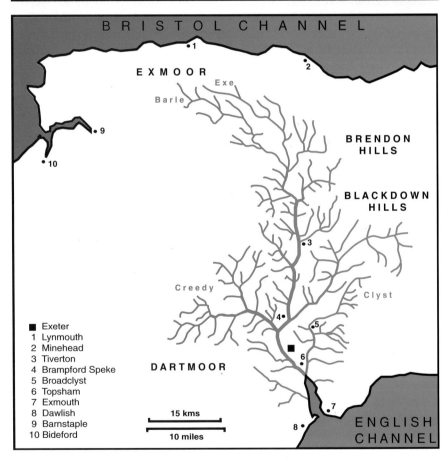

BRISTOL CHANNEL

EXMOOR

Exe

Barle

BRENDON HILLS

BLACKDOWN HILLS

Creedy

Clyst

DARTMOOR

- ■ Exeter
- 1 Lynmouth
- 2 Minehead
- 3 Tiverton
- 4 Brampford Speke
- 5 Broadclyst
- 6 Topsham
- 7 Exmouth
- 8 Dawlish
- 9 Barnstaple
- 10 Bideford

15 kms

10 miles

ENGLISH CHANNEL

Where does the water come from?

The River Exe is fed by waters from many tributaries which, in total, drain an area of about 1300 sq km (800 sq miles). The River Exe itself rises amongst the high land of Exmoor in North Devon. The River Culm drains the Blackdown Hills and the River Creedy carries water in part from the lower slopes of Dartmoor. the system is 90 km (56 miles) long from source to mouth (see map).

The soils are largely resistant (impermeable) to water percolating into the ground and so much of the water falling on the land does not seep (infiltrate) into the soil but runs off quickly towards streams and river. Following heavy rainfall in these high areas, water quickly flows over the often steeply sloping land and find its way into the upper tributaries of the river.

The River Exe may be regarded as a river which has a very rapid response to rainfall. River levels rise very quickly following any heavy downpour. Should heavy rain fall throughout the drainage basin, then there is a real threat of the river overtopping its banks along some stretches of the river.

Flooding in Exeter

Exeter has long suffered flooding from the River Exe. As early as the year 1286 it was recorded that " ..a great part of Exbridge through foul weather and high water, fell down". In 1800, there was "a prodigious flood, such as the oldest person then living had never before witnessed ... all the streets in St Thomas were inundated, the water reaching up to the windows, and these poorer class inhabitants were in great distress ..." . Serious flooding also followed in 1917, 1920, 1929, 1950 and 1952. Yet worse was to come in 1960.

Cowick Street. 4 December 1960.

5

The floods of 1960

It was 'Black Thursday' on 27 October 1960. Over 60 mm (2.4 inches) of rain had fallen the previous day and the river level rapidly rose. The raging River Exe raced into low-lying Exeter at a rate of 700 cubic metres of water per second (9 million gallons a minute). An unstoppable tide of muddy, swirling water burst into homes, shops and factories at lunch-time, cutting the city in half. Flood depths reached two metres (over six feet) in places. When the waters died down the owners of more than 1000 properties had to count the cost. Carpets and clothes were ruined, possessions had been washed away, road surfaces were damaged, walls were toppled, telephones were put out of action and rail services were disrupted as the lines collapsed owing to the ballast being washed away.

For Exeter it was a disaster, demanding a huge emergency operation. Convoys of amphibious vehicles (army DUKWs) evacuated stranded locals - many of whom had been trapped at work. Hundreds of people were unable to return home for the night.

The Exeter flood was one of a series of floods to hit the West Country in 1960 - the third wettest since rainfall records began in 1727. During the autumn of 1960, two-thirds of the average rainfall for the whole year fell in the ten weeks from 27 September to 5 December. Other towns in Devon were also badly damaged by flooding, notably Exmouth and Tiverton. But in Exeter the River Exe struck not once but twice.

Nearly 80 mm (3 inches) of rainfall fell on 3 December, drenching the countryside and turning the River Exe into an angry torrent. The next day, Sunday, 1200 houses and businesses received a miserable soaking from a swollen river - many for the second time.

Right: Map showing the area seriously flooded in December 1960. The main directions in which the flood waters travelled are indicated by black arrows.

Left: A hitch getting to work.

A call for action

The people of Exeter demanded that something be done to prevent a repetition of the 1960 floods. But what were the choices? The public wanted solutions but what were they?

Given an exceptionally wet year again, like 1960, little can be done to prevent the water levels of the tributaries of the River Exe rising. As the tributaries pass the flood waters further downstream, this creates a massive volume of water heading towards Exeter. One can almost visualise a flood wave of rising water surging down the narrow valley of the River Exe towards the city.

In October and December 1960, in the face of the swirling flood waters racing through their city, the people and authorities of Exeter could only take emergency action.

Following those disasters they demanded that flood control planners should ensure the city would cope with the next such occasion without having to resort to desperate emergency measures. They wanted no more suffering from floods.

Photo below:
The Senior Service, Cowick Street, 4 December 1960.

Preventing floods

COST versus RISK

The discharge of a river (the amount of water it transports) is measured in units known as cumecs: an abbreviation for 'cubic metres per second'. Discharge is obtained by measuring the cross-sectional area of a river channel and multiplying this value by the speed of flow of the water. For example, if a river channel is 10 m across and 5 m deep, the cross-sectional area is 10 x 5 = 50 square metres. The speed of flow of the water in the river may be 2 m per second. This means the discharge is 50 x 2 = 100 cumecs (cubic metres per second). In 1960, the maximum amount of water the River Exe channel could carry, before its water overtopped its banks causing floods, varied from about 280 to 450 cumecs (equivalent to about four to six million gallons a minute) for various locations along the river. Following the 1960 floods, designers considered that if flood control measures were to be effective the river channel in the vicinity of Exeter would have to be modified to cope with 700 cumecs, that is, the 1960 flood discharge.

Calculating the risk

Although it seems obvious to select the 1960 flood discharge of 700 cumecs, flood control engineers could have selected a higher or lower value. Using a higher value (say 900 cumecs) for designing flood control structures, would have meant a greater margin of protection for Exeter - but at a greater cost, since the structures would have had to be larger.

Selecting a lower value such as 500 cumecs would have meant cheaper costs but less protection, that is, floods would happen more often and a repetition of the 1960 floods, with all the damage, disruption and distress, was possible.

The front door of the Royal Oak, Okehampton Street, October 1960.

9

Designing for extreme floods

When designing for such extreme flood events one is designing to cope with events that do not happen very often. For example, using the somewhat limited rainfall and river discharge measurements available for the River Exe at the time, it may be suggested that a flood of 700 cumecs may occur on average only once every 50 years. This frequency is the average time elapsing between floods of this magnitude and does not imply that such floods occur regularly every 50 years. A flood of 500 cumecs may occur on average once every 30 years while a flood of 900 cumecs may occur on average only once every 100 years. Communities have to decide up to what level of flood discharge the ontrol system should be designed to protect them. The higher the 'design discharge' the less frequent will the occasions be when the flood control system will be unable to cope - but the higher will be the costs of construction. Decision-makers must balance the risk to people and property against the costs of development. In the case of Exeter, prevention of floods of the 1960 magnitude became the primary objective.

Constructing high 'flood banks' to keep the river within its channel at times of high discharge is one way to control flooding but can you suggest alternative long-term solutions to tackle occasions when the river level rises dramatically? Following the 1960 floods, various approaches to prevent serious flooding were investigated.

Flood prevention: alternative approaches

CHANNEL IMPROVEMENT AND FLOOD BANKS

This was perhaps the most obvious solution. Could the channel of the River Exe be enlarged to cope with the increased water? This would mean deepening and widening the channel and raising the channel sides to produce 'flood banks'. But to widen the river and construct flood banks, parts of the floodplain would have to be cleared of buildings.

Channel improvement on its own was ruled out as a feasible solution to flooding on the River Exe because the maximum size for an improved channel which could be realistically constructed along some stretches of the urban Exe would still only be capable of handling about half of the discharge for which control was needed at times of 'maximum' flood. An improved channel at these points could cope with say 350 cumecs but not 700 cumecs. Consequently, in addition to channel improvement, one or more of the following would be needed:

DIVERSION CHANNELS

Divert the amount of floodwater, with which the River Exe channel could not cope, away from Exeter. For example, a new channel could be constructed north of the city from say, near Brampford Speke and connected eastwards to the River Clyst at Broadclyst (see map on page 4). However, the River Clyst, which meets the coast at Topsham, had its own flood problems. A new river channel would also cut across many roads and railway lines which would require new bridges being built.

STORAGE BASINS

Divert the amount of floodwater, with which the River Exe channel could not cope, into detention reservoirs or storage basins. The problem here was finding sufficiently large areas of, say, low-value agricultural land where floodwater could be stored. In some suitable areas, railway lines had already being built and it would be very expensive and disruptive to raise these lines up onto high embankments.

RELIEF CHANNELS

Divert the amount of floodwater, with which the River Exe channel could not cope, into a second, nearby artificial cutting or flood-relief channel. This could be built in the floodplain and its size could be varied in relation to the capacity of the adjacent River Exe channel such that the two channels could together carry the necessary 700 cumecs.

DIVERSION TUNNELS

Convey the amount of floodwater, with which the River Exe channel could not cope, through one or more tunnels passing from say, near Cowley Bridge under the city to discharge somewhere near Countess Wear. This would take the form of a 6 km (4 mile) long twin-tunnel made up of two 4.6 metre (15 feet) diameter pipes. In the 1960s, not only would this option have been the most costly but technically it posed the greatest difficulties. This solution would have had the least impact on the landscape.

ADDITIONAL MEASURES

There are other measures which can contribute to reducing the flood problem. For example, extensive forests could be planted in the upper parts of the River Exe drainage basin. It has been shown that rain falling onto a forest takes much longer before it eventually reaches the river than rain falling onto grass or bare soil areas. This time-delay prevents the water-level in rivers from rising too quickly so reducing the likelihood of a rapid or flash flood following a heavy rainstorm.

The flood defence scheme proposed

Tunnel rejected

After consideration of the alternative flood control options, the scheme finally advocated in 1962, was improvement to the existing river channel and the construction of a tunnel to take the excess flow during major floods. However, that scheme was not adopted. One reason given was that the capital expenditure required for a tunnel could not be phased over a number of years.

Relief channels favoured

The scheme finally adopted consisted of channel improvements and the construction of relief channels. These measures could be accomplished in distinct stages and the costs spread over several years. Fortunately, given the length of time taken to complete the scheme, a similar flood to 1960 did not occur in the meantime.

Work spread over 14 years

The Devon River Board started construction in 1965. Their successors, the Devon River Authority, continued the work and South West Water finally took over and completed the task in 1979. At 1977 price levels, the River Exe Flood Defence Scheme had cost £8 million. Current responsibility for the scheme lies with the Environment Agency.

Was it the right choice?

Given the impact of the present flood control structures on the riverside landscape and the amount of land it consumes, many people may question whether in retrospect one of the other options, such as a tunnel, would not have been better. You may like to reflect on this during your walk.

Below: The Exwick flood spillway channel in use, 28 December 1979.

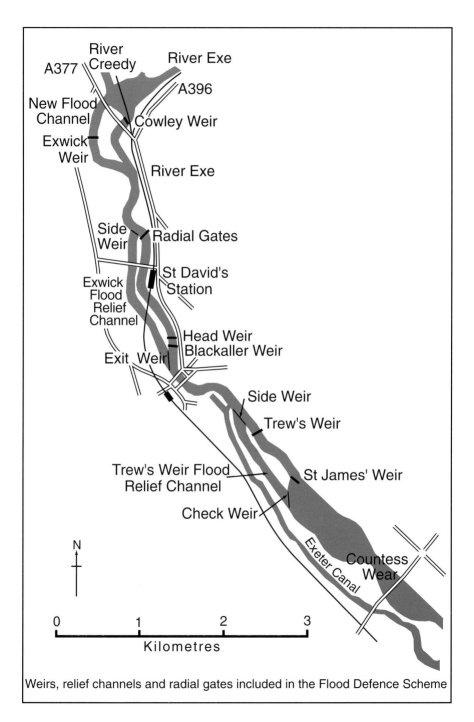

River Creedy

River Exe

A377

A396

New Flood Channel

Cowley Weir

Exwick Weir

River Exe

Side Weir

Radial Gates

St David's Station

Exwick Flood Relief Channel

Head Weir

Blackaller Weir

Exit Weir

Side Weir

Trew's Weir

Trew's Weir Flood Relief Channel

St James' Weir

Check Weir

N

Exeter Canal

Countess Wear

0   1   2   3

Kilometres

Weirs, relief channels and radial gates included in the Flood Defence Scheme

The walk beside the Exe

The Exwick radial gates

Find your position on the map on the previous page. The large concrete and steel structures which lie across the channel at this point are called radial gates. Related to these gates is the narrow concrete wall or side weir which runs for 80 metres or so, upstream from your present location, along the left-hand side of the River Exe and separating it from the beginning of a side channel - although this channel has less water in it than the main river.

The radial gates here at Exwick are a special feature; they close during high flows in the river, limiting the flow of the River Exe downstream to a safe level. Excess flow is diverted over the side weir (see photo on page 12) and down the 1,600 metre long, 26 metre wide side channel (a flood relief channel).

Either by looking at the gates themselves or by examining the designer's blueprints reproduced below, can you work out how the radial gates actually operate automatically so that excess flood-waters are diverted over the side weir and into the relief channel?

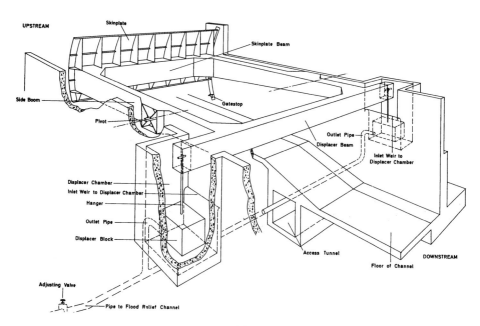

14

The function of the radial gates

Dealing with 700 cumecs

The main channel of the River Exe here can take up to 250 cumecs whereas the relief channel can accommodate 450 cumecs. These two channels together can carry a total flow of 700 cumecs (9 million gallons a minute), equivalent to the worst 1960 flood. The radial gates are designed so that the relief channel begins to be used when the river flow reaches 180 cumecs.

Operated by water levels

The radial gates are operated by changes in water-level, and so are not susceptible to power failures which often occur in storm and flood conditions. The gates lower only to within 830 mm (2 feet 9 inches) of the river bed to prevent a tranquil area of water developing behind the gates, which would cause sediment deposition immediately upstream of the structure. Floating objects and debris can pass through the centre flumed section at all times.

Why two channels?

Some consideration was given as to whether it would have been better to have built a completely new 700 cumec channel at this location rather than maintain the existing river channel as well as constructing a relief channel. Given the disruption that construction of a complete new and very large channel might cause, it was decided that the twin-channel system, as seen today, was preferable.

Flooding the chambers

When the River Exe channel reaches a discharge of 180 cumecs its surface is equivalent to an ordnance datum, mean sea level, height of 11.0 metres (notice the vertical scale near each radial gate float). At this level, water will begin to flood the two chambers containing the radial gate floats. As each float rises, the radial gate lowers because the structure is pivoted. This movement is made easier by having small wheels on the sides of each radial gate.

Sharing the river flow

The two radial gates partially block the main channel which means some of the river flow will overtop the side weir and pass down the relief channel. The result is that the radial gates share out the river flow and prevent either channel from exceeding its capacity - as long as the combined discharge does not exceed 700 cumecs.

Testing out the system

The radial gates system was originally tested and refined using a small-scale model at the Hydraulics Research Station at Wallingford, Oxfordshire. The photos show the model in operation. You are standing at location X? Testing models under extreme conditions can provide valuable information on the safety margins of the system and can also save money by identifying design faults early and demonstrating how the system can operate most effectively. In this case model testing showed that the system operated most efficiently without having a third set of radial gates in the middle section as had been originally planned.

Here the model is being successfully tested at the equivalent to its maximum design discharge of 708 cumecs (25,000 cubic feet per second), the 1960 flood discharge.

Walking south by the river

Now return to the gate leading onto Station Road. Cross the road. Ahead is another gate which leads to a flat-topped grassed area with a path close to the water's edge. Walk south along this grass bank which separates the main River Exe channel (on your left) and the Exwick Flood Relief Channel (on your right). If it is not too wet, keep to the higher grassed areas for the time-being, rather than the path.

What is the purpose of the grass bank seen on the other side of the Exwick relief channel?

Clearly, the grass bank, like the one you were previously standing on, has been artificially raised. It was raised by about 2 metres using material excavated from the relief channel. Use of this material had the advantage of avoiding costly haulage.

The bank forms a flood-protection bank or simply, a flood bank. It prevents water in the relief channel from overtopping and causing flooding of the streets and houses of Exwick.

Exwick suffered very severely in the 1960 floods. The old Station Road bridge was a major river obstruction and diverted floodwaters into the Exwick district. The bridge was eventually washed away in 1974 during construction of the Flood Relief Channel. In 1960, mud, silt, debris and even boulders swept through the streets and houses were flooded to a depth of one metre and even two metres in places.

Notice that the first floors of many of the newer Exwick houses are lower than the flood bank. Many of these houses have been built since 1960 and reflect the sense of security that the wide flood bank has given residents against the threat of renewed flooding.

The high bank you are standing on separates the main river channel and the relief channel. It is not a flood bank as such but maximises the volume of water that each channel can carry.

Continue walking south but pause as you pass under the railway bridge.

Bridges

At this point, a railway bridge passes over both the main channel of the River Exe (on your left when facing downstream) and the Exwick relief channel (on your right). Perhaps you can identify this bridge on the map on page 13?

The piers or buttresses supporting a bridge inevitably act as obstructions to the flow of water. Floodwaters are notorious for the debris they carry and any obstructions in the river channel can cause blockages as debris and branches get caught. Compare the piers of the section of the bridge over the main channel of the river with that over the relief channel.

At times of turbulence, resulting in debris-laden floodwaters, which section of bridge would you suppose is likely to cause the most obstruction?

Obstruction by the bridge

There is a marked difference in the shapes of the piers of the two bridges seen from this point. Clearly the bridge over the Exwick relief channel has been designed to cause minimal obstruction. Its modern piers have streamlined shapes and the underside of the bridge is curved to allow easier passage of floodwaters.

In contrast, the railway bridge over the main river channel has large rounded piers and a lattice-work girder structure. Although such an overall design makes it a greater obstacle to floodwaters than the modern bridge, it was deemed not so great an obstruction that it justified the cost of a replacement.

There is a further complication when considering which bridge is likely to cause the worse obstruction. This is whether the floodwaters in the main channel would have more or less debris in it than the relief channel, given the presence of the radial gates (which you visited earlier).

Continue walking along this 'island' between the main river channel and the Exwick relief channel.

Landscaping

Considerable attention has been given to landscaping this area. Extensive smooth and well-grassed areas have been created. The water level in the Exwick relief channel, when not in use as a flood channel, is maintained at a set height. Paved walkways have been built along the relief channel.

Apart from its flood relief function, what other purposes could this channel be used for?

Making use of the flood relief channel

Since its completion in 1976 the Exwick relief channel has been exploited for recreation with windsurfing, model boating, water skiing and canoeing. There is usually water in the channel with an average depth of 0.7 metres at the upstream end and 1.7 metres at the downstream end. Walkways and picnic tables add to the leisure-time attraction of the area. Playing fields have been created on the grassy areas. An information board is provided at the upstream end of the channel.

Are there ways in which this area could be further improved for leisure and recreation activities?

Improvements

Some people may dislike the artificial nature of the landscape although some aspects of this have to be maintained so as to fulfil its purpose for flood relief. Perhaps more trees, shrubs and flowers would make the area appear more 'natural'? Some may regret the extensive use of concrete surfaces for the relief channel but designers argued this was necessary to permit steeper sides than could be achieved by grass (which might slump) and so reduce the width of the channel needed. Above the steep channel slopes the land has been grassed. Some problems can be tackled, for example, the tranquil waters of the channel encourage the growth of weeds and the collection of debris. Regular removal of this would maintain a clean-looking waterway.

What do you think?

Given the present open access to the very steep banks of the channel, some people may like to see the area made safer for young children. Others might wish for toilets, cafés and a shop from which to hire windsurfing boards. More benches could be added and more information boards giving some of the area's history could be erected. Would you agree?

Weirs

Continue to the end of the Exwick flood relief channel. To your right is a footbridge which spans the relief channel. To your left is the new (2002) Millers cycle and footbridge (see photo). The 50 m cabled span is anchored to a massive 'mill wheel' feature via a 20 m high steel pylon. From here, look at the main channel of the River Exe. Built on the river bed are two low barriers or weirs over which the river rushes. Upstream is the 'Head Weir'. Downstream is the 'Blackaller Weir'. Why were weirs built? One reason may be clear from the map below.

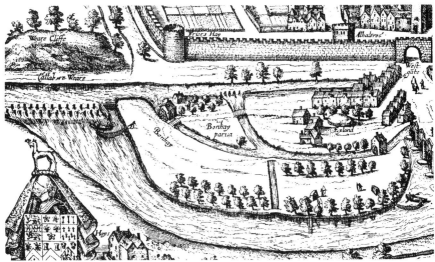

An early weir at this location from a map of 1618.

Weirs and their uses

A weir may be built for a variety of purposes. You have seen the side weir at the start of the Exwick flood relief channel which, together with the radial gates, controls the level at which river water begins to overflow into the relief channel. On many of our country's rivers, you may also have seen weirs used in connection with lock gates which provide passage for river boats and barges. Weirs may also be employed to limit the stretch of river subjected to tidal flow. They may also control water levels in sections of rivers or streams used for fishing.

Weirs on the Exe

The weirs on this stretch of the Exe were originally built several centuries ago to raise the level of the river upstream of the weir and create a head of water for a leat or watercourse on which were located water-wheels to produce water power. A leat left the river at this point on the river, across the other side of the channel from where you are now standing, and led southwards along the city wall following the foot of the red sandstone cliffs. It was called the Head or Higher Leat and was one of several leats constructed to drain the marshy land, called Exe Island, that lay between the city wall and the river downstream from this location.

The leats provided many sites on which mills and factories could be built and operated using water power. At this location, the Head Weir was angled across the river so as to direct water along the Head Leat. For many centuries a large mill existed here (see photographs on front cover and on page 23). Originally it was a fulling-mill where woollen cloth was pounded and scoured to thicken the fabric whilst being cleaned. The building later became a papermill. The only clues to this past activity evident today are a metal grill along the river bank through which water enters, and the riverside inn called 'Mill on the Exe' on the site of the old mill.

W alk to the middle of the new bridge and look upstream. As noted earlier, the land to the left of the river forms a wide gently sloping surface stretching away to the west, towards Exwick. It is a typical floodplain. However, on the right-hand (eastern) side of the river the land rises dramatically from close to the riverside to form a steep cliff. How was this cliff created?

Meanders and river cliffs

River meanders

Rivers in spate constantly erode alluvium from their banks, often redepositing it a short way downstream. This tends to cause meanders to 'migrate' both downstream and from side to side within their floodplain. The tendency for meanders to snake about the floodplain is quite natural. It might, therefore, be considered an appropriate management strategy to keep the floodplain free from development, allowing meanders to change their location within the floodplain without interference.

However, in an urban setting this is rarely a management option, since development, in the form of quays and buildings, had often already taken place long before river management was a consideration. In towns and cities, therefore, rivers are often constrained within the shape they had at the time when the riverfront was first developed.

River cliffs

When free to scythe back and forth across the floodplain, river meanders will often impinge on the valley sides, extending the floodplain by undercutting the country rock which becomes unstable and collapses, exposing a steep, fresh-faced slope, a 'river cliff'. The 'cliff' on the right was cut by the Exe before the relatively modern construction of Bonhay Road constrained the river.

The river cliff clearly exposes the local Carboniferous country rock, here steeply dipping and faulted sandstones, siltstones and shale. It is a site of special scientific interest (SSSI). A brief diversion across the bridge and a walk a few metres upstream would give you safe road-side views of the outcrop together with an interpretation panel, provided by English Nature, nearby. For more detail of the 'Bonhay Road Cutting' visit the Educational Register of Geological Sites at: http://www.devon.gov.uk/geology.

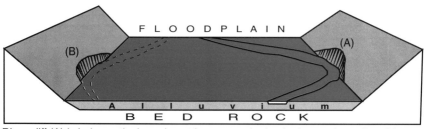

River cliff (A) is being actively undercut by a meander impinging on the valley side.
River cliff (B) is a relict feature cut when the river was meandering on the far side.

The Exe in spate at Blackaller Weir, 28 December 1979. The papermill shown here, once the site of a fulling mill, has since been dismantled, its place being taken by the riverside inn, 'The Mill on the Exe'.

Now return to the path and cross the single-span, steel, box-girder footbridge which spans the Exwick relief channel.

Note the exit weir and stilling basin at the end of the Exwick flood relief channel. The weir maintains a minimum depth of water in the relief channel. This arrangement also reduces the speed at which the water flows out of the relief channel when rejoining the main river channel preventing scouring of the river bed and banks downstream.

Continue south along the footpath as it follows the wide meander bend of the River Exe channel towards a modern road-bridge. Before you reach the bridge, look out for the back of the 'Royal Oak' public house (at the top of the river bank on your right). Climb the bank just past this public house and look back (to your right) along the adjacent street (Okehampton Street).

23

Okehampton Street

A t this point, compare your view with the photograph below, taken on this same stretch of Okehampton Street on 27 October 1960.

Some of the nearby buildings on both sides of the street have been demolished since the photograph was taken but the terraced houses in the distance can be matched. The tops of their front-garden brick walls are just visible in the flood photograph. The dramatic absence of the high, protective river bank separating Okehampton Street and the river channel is very evident in the flood photograph.

A raging torrent in Okehampton Street. The 'Royal Oak' is on the right.

If you had lived here in 1960 and had received a warning from the police and/or local radio that your house was likely to flood in a few hours time, what action would you personally have taken?

A flood alert

Personal preparations

With a possible flood likely in a few hours there is little opportunity to take much more than emergency action. Such action may include:

(a) closing windows and doors, placing sandbags, or some other form of barrier, across doorways and other openings (such as air-bricks) through which water might flow;
(b) moving possessions upstairs;
(c) switching off electricity and gas to prevent fire/explosions;
(d) drawing off some clean drinkingwater;
(e) moving outside possessions such as a car, garden furniture, rabbit hutch, etc. to a safer location; and
(f) evacuating the building.

Flood warnings

Compared with 1960, the Environment Agency today is able to obtain up-to-the-minute information not only on the current level of the River Exe at Exeter but on river levels and rainfall rates throughout the River Exe drainage basin.

This information is analysed by the Flood Forecasting and Warning Centre at Exeter so as to provide decisions on river-flow regulation at weir-sluices and whether flood warnings need to be issued. These warnings are issued to the Police, Local Authorities, residents likely to be affected and to other organisations which have an interest, such as the Water Companies (see diagram overleaf). If exceptionally heavy rain fell over the upper part of the River Exe, say over Exmoor, flood forecasting could provide a flood warning time of up to six hours.

Today, as a result of the extensive flood control measures undertaken since 1960, Okehampton Street and other areas of Exeter should be well protected from serious flooding.

The period 1960 to 2003

The new control measures have been severely tested twice since 1960.

In February 1978 between 0.5 and 1.0 metre of snow fell over Devon. The subsequent thaw, induced by heavy rain, produced a discharge at Exeter of 400 cumecs - slightly over half the design discharge of the Flood Control System. There were no reports of floods in the Exeter area.

October 2000 saw 90 mm (3.5 inches) of rainfall on Exmoor produce a discharge at Exeter of 500 cumecs. There was spare capacity through Exeter although some flooding in the unprotected areas downstream of the scheme was recorded.

25

How flood warnings work

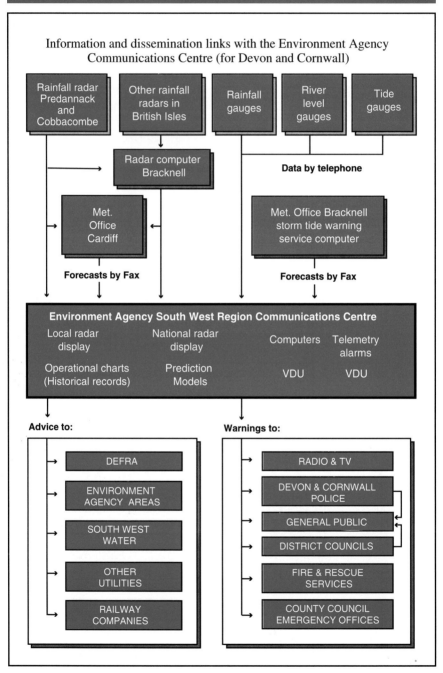

Information and dissemination links with the Environment Agency Communications Centre (for Devon and Cornwall)

Rainfall radar Predannack and Cobbacombe

Other rainfall radars in British Isles

Rainfall gauges

River level gauges

Tide gauges

Radar computer Bracknell

Data by telephone

Met. Office Cardiff

Met. Office Bracknell storm tide warning service computer

Forecasts by Fax

Forecasts by Fax

Environment Agency South West Region Communications Centre

Local radar display

National radar display

Computers   Telemetry alarms

Operational charts (Historical records)

Prediction Models

VDU   VDU

Advice to:

Warnings to:

Advice to:	Warnings to:
DEFRA	RADIO & TV
ENVIRONMENT AGENCY AREAS	DEVON & CORNWALL POLICE
SOUTH WEST WATER	GENERAL PUBLIC
OTHER UTILITIES	DISTRICT COUNCILS
RAILWAY COMPANIES	FIRE & RESCUE SERVICES
	COUNTY COUNCIL EMERGENCY OFFICES

Exe Bridge North

Continue towards the modern road-bridge which is called **Exe Bridge North.** As you approach the modern bridge, notice the two narrow streamlined piers which support this bridge. These were designed to minimise obstruction to the river flow. Similar piers support its twin bridge, Exe Bridge South, just a short distance downstream. **Stop in the middle of Exe Bridge North.** A bridge across the River Exe has existed close to this site since the 13th century. When was the bridge you are standing on built?

The new Exe Bridge North, where you are now standing, being built in 1968. Notice the coffer dams erected around the piers of the new bridge during construction. In the middle distance is the old Exe Bridge, built in 1905 and finally dismantled in 1973.

The Twin Exe Bridge Scheme

Exe Bridge North was opened on 30 July 1969 and was the first of the twin bridges to be completed. Exe Bridge South was completed in the early 1970s and these twin bridges replaced the famous 1905 steel arch Exe Bridge (seen on the previous page) designed by Sir John Wolfe Barry, an engineer famous for his Tower Bridge in London. One reason for its replacement was the traffic bottle-neck it created.

Exe Bridge was the gateway to the south coast of Devon and Cornwall and serious traffic congestion regularly resulted. The old bridge could not cope so the opportunity to replace it with two bridges was taken. This allowed a more satisfactory traffic layout to be constructed with the bridges forming two sides of a roundabout centred over the river. Each bridge spans about 67 metres (220 feet).

Apart from traffic congestion, what other reasons were there for replacing the 1905 Exe Bridge?

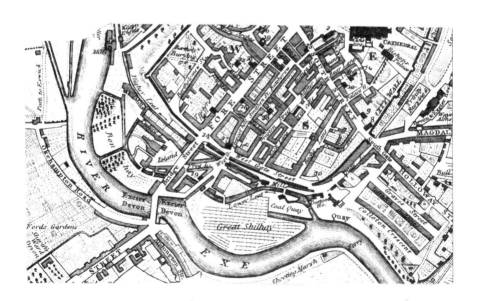

Above: An even older Exe Bridge on a map of 1805.

The plan for the Twin Exe Bridge scheme 1967-1973

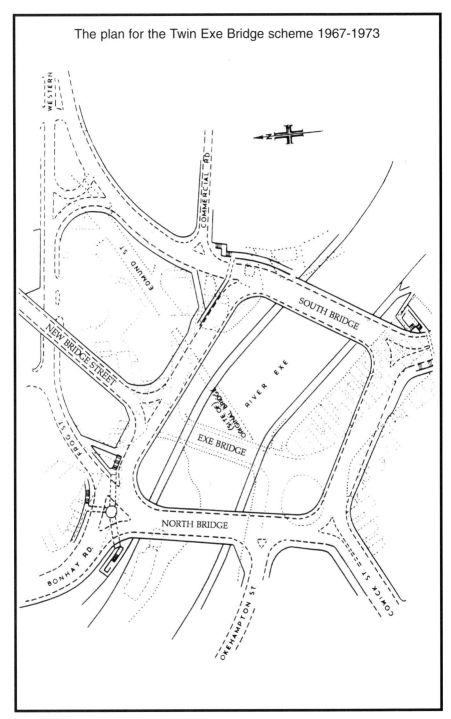

The completed twin Exe Bridge scheme. Note the way the long piers of the new bridges reflect the gentle meandering sweep of the Exe. The tower of St Edmund's Church and the remains of the medieval bridge suggest something of the former width of the Exe floodplain at this point.

Why build a new bridge?

Preventing floods, as well as relieving traffic congestion, figured in the decision to replace the old Exe Bridge, as:

(a) the existing river-channel at this point caused a constriction and it needed to be widened and deepened. The old bridge had a span of 46 metres (150 feet) and the channel needed widening to 55 metres (180 feet) in order to increase the river capacity here by 25%;

(b) the steel arch bridge posed too great an obstruction itself, especially when the river level rose and reached the upper structure;

(c) the sweeping meander of the river immediately upstream of the bridge meant that the forces of erosion were particularly active on the St Thomas side of the river. The meander of the channel needed reshaping; and

(d) the 1960 floods raised the question of the safety of the old bridge under repeated severe flood conditions. The turbulent, debris-laden floodwaters had caused the bridge to vibrate and the bridge may have suffered structural damage from being struck repeatedly by heavy floating debris.

Now continue across the bridge. Turn left into the pedestrian subway at the end of the bridge under Bonhay Road. In the subway, proceed straight across under the City Centre sign. Go up the steps directly ahead and out into the open. Bear left and pause briefly before going through the arch beneath New Bridge Street.

This arch was the approach to both the iron 1905 Exe Bridge and the earlier 1778 bridge. New Bridge Street was built as an extension to Fore Street, breaching the city wall, to join up to the Exe Bridge, giving direct, if rather steep, access to the city centre. Horse-drawn carriages found this street particularly difficult.

As you walk from under the archway of New Bridge Street, you will see the old medieval stone bridge uncovered during the completion of the two new modern bridges.

Explore the medieval bridge! It was built around the year 1258 and is the earliest surviving large stone bridge in the country. Of the original 16-18 arches, eight and a half still remain. Why should the bridge have been so long?

The Medieval Stone Bridge

Above: A drawing of St Edmund's Church tower and remaining arches of the medieval bridge (Margaret Peters 1991).

A very long bridge

The bridge was of such a length because not only did it have to cross the river channel but also the extensive marshland that formed the river's floodplain (as implied by the local name of Marsh Barton). Some attempts had been made to drain this marshland which lay outside the city walls but progress was slow. Beginning in the tenth century, a series of leats or waterways were constructed. Construction of the Head or Higher Leat and draining and infilling of this land created Exe Island on which you are standing and this, of course, reduced the river's natural floodplain.

Bridges cost money

The building of the medieval Exe Bridge was due largely to the wealthy thirteenth century merchant, Nicolas Gervaise and his son, who became the city mayor. They raised the money to build the bridge and purchased property to provide an annual income for its future maintenance. Houses existed on the bridge in the thirteenth and fourteenth centuries and St Edmund's Church was an integral part of the bridge. The houses were owned by the Exe Bridge Trust, set up by Walter Gervaise, to provide an income to maintain the bridge.

Below: The medieval Exe Bridge drawn by W. Schellinker 1662.

A history of replacing bridges

Owing to the increased volume of traffic, the narrow medieval bridge had become very congested by the mid-eighteenth century. In 1770, Joseph Dixon designed and began building a new bridge, of three arches only, in a direct line from Fore Street to Cowick Street (see maps on pages 28 and 29). Work was well advanced when on Monday 18 January 1775, a tremendous flood .... *"entirely destroyed the foundations and carried away all the arches of the new bridge, and greatly terrified the neighbouring inhabitants lest it should damage the old bridge."*

Despite the setback, the £30,000 bridge was completed and open to traffic by 1778. New Bridge Street gave access to the bridge along a raised embankment, pierced by arches over Frog Street and the Higher and Lower Mill-leats.

The eighteenth century bridge was subsequently replaced by a 540-ton, iron bridge which was opened by Mayor E.C.Perry on 29 March 1905. The new bridge was built nearly four metres (11 feet) wider than its predecessor and being a flat bridge (rather than arched) it was easier for electric trams to use. Electric trams had been introduced into the city in April of that year to compete with the horse-drawn trams in existence since the 1880s.

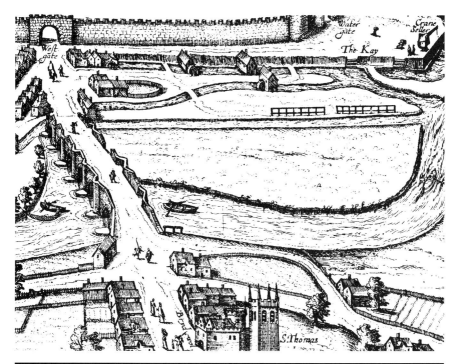

Above: Exe Bridge as shown on a map of 1618 (from Braun and Hoghenbergh's 'Civitates Orbis Terrarum'). The bridge is viewed from the west, from St Thomas, looking towards the west gate. Various leats, utilised by water mills, rejoin the Exe at the Quay (The Kay). Fishermen are active on the upstream side of the bridge.

Left: A Victorian drawing by S.Townsend reconstructing the probable appearance of the medieval buildings integrated into the old stone bridge.

Walking towards the Quay

Leave the medieval bridge at the top level (at the River Exe end) and take the pedestrian subway on your left which will lead you towards the Exeter Quay and Canal Basin. Take the right-hand ramp to the surface. Immediately turn left at the start of Exe Bridge South so that you can follow the riverside path downstream (signposted 'Riverside Walks and Quay').

Shilhay and flood banks

As you walk along the riverside path pause to look towards the buildings on your left.

These new properties are built on an area called the Shilhay (Shilley or Shillhay) which was once the industrial heartland of Exeter with many cloth mills, iron foundries, timber-yards, tanneries, warehouses, factories, coal-yards and assorted businesses. The floodplain here, as shown on the 1723 map (below), was once covered with drying racks associated with the cloth mills. The land has since been raised and the houses are built on top of this raised land which forms a flood bank protecting the houses against unduly high river levels.

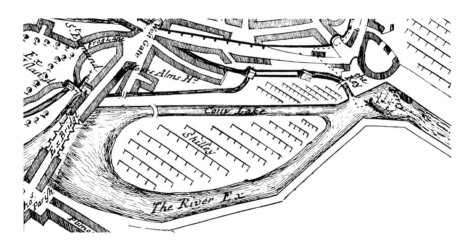

Map: The Shilley in 1723. Note the racks used for drying cloth after fulling and dyeing. The racks are also clearly shown on the 1805 map (page 28).

This stretch of the river proved a problem to the flood control planners as there was not enough undeveloped land available to build a relief channel. Consequently they had to rely on measures taken a little further downstream at Trew's Weir as well as deepening the river and raising the banks here as much as possible.

The District of St Thomas

Across the river is the district of St Thomas which suffered from very serious flooding in 1960 (see map on page 7). This area also used to experience minor flooding of streets and some houses during each winter even when the river did NOT actually overtop its banks.

What can cause streets and houses to flood even though the river does NOT overtop its banks?

Riverside flooding

Heavy rainfall

There may be occasions following heavy rain when the drainage system in a built-up area cannot cope. In 1960, St Thomas was serviced by an inadequate main drainage system in this low-lying district, which caused shallow and very unpleasant flooding even without the river overflowing its banks.

If river levels were high they prevented the drains from transferring their waters into the river and the foul water backed up into streets and houses.

Improved drainage

After 1960, an important flood control measure for this area was to improve its drainage. Together with Exwick in the north-west and Marsh Barton in the south-east, a new surface-water sewerage system was installed which discharged much lower downstream, below St James' Weir. This left the existing sewers to carry sewage to the purification works. A main intercepting sewer was laid along the foot of the steeply sloping hills, to intercept stormwater prior to its discharge along the sewers in the flat low-lying land. In addition, a subsidiary main sewer was laid through the central portion of the area. The sewer pipes ranged in diameter from 0.6 metre (24 inch) to 1.8 metres (72 inch) and the total cost of the improvement in drainage was £1 million.

Continue along the riverside path around the meander bend. An impressive suspension bridge spans the river ahead. From its style can you guess approximately when it was built?

Exeter Quay

The footbridge crossing the river is called Cricklepit Bridge named after a nearby building known as Cricklepit Mill. Although built in Victorian style, the bridge was only built in 1988. It was intended to provide a bridge which was in keeping with the character of the quayside buildings; do you think this attempt was successful?

Do not cross the footbridge but continue along the riverside path over Mallison Bridge (1984). The leat beneath Mallison Bridge which runs beside the city wall is surprisingly ancient and occurs in many earlier maps of Exeter, including 1618 map illustrated on pages 20, 35 and 42. It is known as the Higher Leat and was the outlet for the series of leats which originally created Exe Island.

Walk past the open-sided Transit Shed. This was built in 1820 (restored in 1988) to provide undercover storage for cargo being transferred to and from sea-going vessels lying alongside Exeter Quay. It also provided cover for a fish market. Behind the Shed lies the splendid Custom House (completed in 1682) at the foot of Quay Hill which rises up to the city. Three hundred years ago the Quay was a hive of activity as coal, wool, timber, tea, coffee, wines, spirits and spices arrived.

The decline of the port

Exeter Quay, as we see it today, was mainly constructed in the seventeenth century when major improvements made Exeter a viable seaport. The warehouses which dominate the Quay were built in 1835 to cope with the enormous amount of trade from the 20-30 vessels using the Quay at any one time. The port began to decline in importance when competition for trade from the railways developed in the 1840s.

Exeter Quay has become a popular tourist spot and you may recognise it from its frequent use as a film set for historical films and television dramas. For example, it portrayed Liverpool in the television series 'The Onedin Line' in the 1970s.

Photo below: 'New' development on Haven Banks (April 1991).

What is picturesque?

The survival of the Quay to become a picturesque tourist trap may be regarded as one of the more beneficial by-products of the Quay's industrial decline. As Cherry and Pevsner ('Buildings of England; Devon' 1989) suggest, it is, "... one of Exeter's most delightful spots", although they are critical of the "... overmuch clutter of would-be-picturesque street furniture". You may have thought the design of the suspension bridge blended well with the architectural atmosphere of the quayside, but the new development of Haven Banks on the far side of the river may need to mellow a little before being regarded in the same light. The mix of continental style piazza, shops, waterside restaurants, hotel and homes was described by the Deputy Chief Planning Officer as "... imaginative, urban in scale and reflecting the area's riverside character". Do you agree?

Above: The Quay and warehouses of 1835 (Margaret Peters 1991).
Below: "One of Exeter's most delightful spots." (photo 1991).

Walking south from the Quay

Continue downstream along the Quay Path. Notice the two ornate decorated lamps erected adjacent to the manually-operated, wire-guided ferry on the Quay. These are two of six lamps which were originally on the 1905 iron Exe Bridge. The manually-operated ferry has a much longer history and there are records of such a ferry dating back to 1750.

Continue southwards along a riverside footpath, passing the Victorian 'Port Royal Inn' on your left after about 100 metres.

In places, some of the river water passes through private sluice gates which once served factories involved in cotton spinning and paper making.

The weir ahead over which the River Exe rushes is called Trew's Weir. Beyond the weir is another suspension bridge and this will be the next stop. Although it may briefly swing away from the river bank, follow the footpath and then branch sharp right taking the path which leads you to the suspension bridge, built in 1935. Stop near the middle of the bridge.

Can you find your present location on the air photo on the front cover of the book? Looking upstream from the bridge you can see the river tumbling over Trew's Weir which stretches nearly all the way across the main channel.

Trew's Weir

The original weir at this location, St Leonard's Weir, was made of stakes and brushwood, but was rebuilt in the 1560s to create a head of water for the Exeter Canal begun by a Welsh engineer, John Trew.

Above: St Leonard's Weir, the entrance to the Exeter Canal (New haven) and the Quay as shown on the map of 1618.

Fine-tuning the river

In flood conditions, Trew's Weir allows 340 cumecs to flow over it. Viewed from the suspension bridge note that at the left-hand side of the weir is a sluice gate (with a maximum capacity of 100 cumecs) and control works. The 6.1 metre wide by 3.5 metre high radial gate of this sluice acts as the fine-tuner of river flow in this location.

Further to your left is the Trew's Weir relief channel. This channel is usually dry but the front cover photograph was taken when the relief channel was recently in use. The relief channel has a maximum capacity of 260 cumecs. This channel has its entrance, a side weir, immediately upstream of the sluice gate and its exit downstream from St James' Weir (further downstream and out of sight).

Coping with 700 cumecs

At this point you may like to glance back to page 13 to see how this element of river control at Trew's Weir fits into a sequence of constructions along the river.

The combination of structures here ensures that the river at this point can cope with an extreme flood of 700 cumecs. It also ensures that under lesser flows it can maintain an acceptable water level in the upstream reach of the River Exe. The system also has the effect of reducing the height of the flood banks required as far upstream as Blackaller Weir.

A fish pass has been constructed on the sluice island here and this provides a safe passage for those fish which are attracted into the sluice tailrace by the strong flow of water there.

St James' Weir

The next weir downstream on the River Exe, not visible from here, but seen on the map on page 13, is St James' Weir. This weir is subject to the influence of the tide which, at times of exceptionally high tides, can aggravate flooding along the River Exe. When tidal interference is at its maximum, and the river here is in flood, the tail water (the water immediately downstream of the weir) can rise to a level higher than the crest of the weir.

Continue across the walkway until you can see down into Trew's Weir flood relief channel.

Why is the flood relief channel grass-covered downstream but lined with concrete upstream?

The relief channel weir at Trew's Weir from the end of the Exeter Canal (Drawing by Margaret Peters 1991).

43

Trew's Weir flood relief channel

The flood relief channel is not in use for much of the year so it is preferable to maintain this extensive area looking as pleasing as possible. Grass cover is considerably more pleasant than concrete - and it is cheaper. In general, the grass section successfully merges into the landscape. At the upstream end of the relief channel, by the foot of the side weir, is the stilling basin. This has a concrete floor to withstand the flow of water falling over the side weir. The side weir operates two or three times a year in the winter months.

Looking back (with hindsight?)

1960 a turning point

The year 1960 was a significant year for the people of Exeter. Although it was the year that many suffered miserably from flooding, it marked a turning point with regard to the city's flood problem. Never again has the city had to suffer serious and extensive flooding. This is due entirely to the flood control structures and improvements to the river, seen along this walk. The River Exe Flood Defence Scheme has operated successfully on many occasions, for example, when coping with a river flow of 400 cumecs in February 1978, produced by deep-lying snow melting rapidly during heavy rainfall, and again in October 2000 when 500 cumecs was contained within the scheme.

The changes made to the river and its floodplain have radically changed the riverside landscape. The massive flood relief channels and the extensive high flood banks are now a permanent part of Exeter. They are seen by Exeter residents and visitors whenever they walk or drive near the river. Many people visit the riverside for leisure and recreation activities.

Alternatives

The riverside landscape would have been very different had an alternative flood alleviation scheme been followed. At the start of this trail it was mentioned that the original plan was to improve the River Exe channel and to build a tunnel to carry the excess floodwaters rather than construct relief channels. The tunnel would have removed the excess water upstream of Exeter and have carried it under the city to join the River Exe downstream of St James' Weir. One wonders what the riverside landscape would have looked like if such a plan had been adopted. The twin Exe Bridges would still have been built but there would have been no Exwick or Trew's Weir relief channels and probably lower flood banks along the Exe. The River Exe would have been tamed, but in a different way.

magine if the floods had not happened in 1960 but had happened, say, last year. Consider whether you would have opted for the Flood Defence Scheme that exists now or would you have preferred an alternative scheme?

Continue along the path, turning right to walk alongside the Exeter Canal on your left and then pause after crossing the first footbridge.

Navigation

Navigating the Exe

In earlier times it was possible to navigate the River Exe from the sea as far as Exeter but because of rivalry with the city, the Earls of Devon blocked the river with a weir at the village of Countess Wear so cutting off the city from the sea.

A weir had existed at Countess Wear since 1284, built by Isabella de Fortibus, Countess of Devon. This earlier weir had a gap so that shipping could pass through to Exeter but a successor, Hugh de Courtenay, blocked the passageway, forcing ships to offload at Topsham. The Earls of Devon owned lands which included the port of Topsham so they subjected offloaded goods to tolls.

The Exeter Canal

This situation led to substantial loss of revenue for the city so plans were drawn up to construct a canal to bypass the weir. John Trew began the Exeter Canal in 1564 with a shallow stretch of canal that went from here to Countess Wear, where vessels rejoined the river

below the weir. This earlier canal could only take small boats so cargo was unloaded from sea-going vessels anchored off Topsham and taken by canal to the city. The canal was subsequently enlarged and extended, first in 1675 to Topsham and then in 1827 to Turf. The Canal Basin at Exeter was completed in 1830.

Today the canal is eight kilometres (five miles) long and five metres (fifteen feet) deep. It was the first 'pound lock' canal in England, this being the now common system of vessels being elevated by being impounded between double lock gates.

In the 1840s the canal trade suffered a decline due to competition from the railways, especially when the Exeter St David's railway station was opened in 1844. Regular commercial canal trade ceased in 1972 when the Esso Depot at Exeter was closed and canal and river use became recreational.

Walking back to Exeter Quay

Turn right, before the second footbridge, to walk along the Quay with the Canal Basin on your left. The Canal Basin was constructed by James Green in 1830 to take large vessels. The basin was formerly the home of the Maritime Museum. A selection of the larger vessels kept in the basin by the museum can be seen in the photograph below, taken in about 1990.

This is a convenient point to end the guided walk. You can return to the city centre or the start of the walk by crossing the river by way of Cricklepit Bridge or, in summer, on the manually operated ferry at the Quay. Alternatively, by crossing Cricklepit Bridge and Exe Bridge South you will come to Exeter St Thomas' railway station, should you wish to return to the start of the walk by a short train journey.

Are you at risk?

- If you live near a river or on a floodplain it is likely that your house has a measurable risk of flooding, although this risk might be quite small.
- If you live in England and Wales you can see instantly where the areas of flood risk are, either from rivers or the sea.
- Try accessing the Environment Agency website by logging on to: www.environment-agency.gov.uk - then look under the floods section.

FLOODING. YOU CAN'T PREVENT IT. YOU CAN PREPARE FOR IT.

Floodline
0845 988 1188
ENVIRONMENT AGENCY

The Environment Agency has several publications on steps people can take before, during and after a flood, available on request from Floodline. For copies, further information, help or advice, contact Environment Agency 'Floodline' 0845 988 1188 (phone calls are charged at the local rate) or email: enquiries@environment-agency.gov.uk

Follow up

Further Exeter walks

There are other parts of the River Exe Flood Defence Scheme which you could visit another day. In effect, the flood control scheme is a system stretching 11 km (7 miles) from the Water Treatment Works at Pynes to the Countess Wear Sewage Treatment Works.

At Cowley there have been major improvements to the river including construction of a 400-metre earth flood relief channel.

Comparing floods

Thematic Trails (see page 49) has published two other booklets by the same authors examining two contrasting areas that have suffered serious flooding.

'Taming the Rivers of Oxford'
'Lyn in Flood, Watersmeet to Lynmouth'

Rain falling on Exmoor a short distance north of the source of the Exe, drains northwards to Lynmouth (see map page 4) via boulder-strewn streams entrenched in deep wooded valleys. The Lyn system is in vivid contrast to the wide meandering Exe, yet here too, events, including the catastrophic flood of 15 August 1952, have dictated that the river must be managed.

A record of floods at Exeter

From "Antiquities of the City of Exeter" (Richard Izacke, 1676)

1250 Walter Gervis a worthy citizen hereof founded Exbridge (the ferry being here formerly kept).

1286 A great part of Exbridge through foul weather and high water, fell down and again soon repaired.

1384 A great part of Exbridge by means of high water fell down, and sundry persons therewith destroyed.

1447 Exbridge was now in great decay, the stonework thereof being much foundred and the higher part being all of timber was consumed and worn away.

1539 About the end of November one of the middle of arches of Exbridge fell down and was again speedily erected by the Bridge Warden.

1625 A tremendous flood swept through the valley, causing great devastation. In the town of Tiverton alone 53 houses were destroyed.

From sundry records of Exeter and district

1757 As the result of extremely heavy overnight rain the Exe rose suddenly. Many bridges were destroyed or damaged throughout the Exe Valley.

1775 The foundations and arches of the new Exe Bridge were badly damaged. There was devastation throughout the valley and the poor suffered much distress.

1786 Owing to the great fall of rain the rivers were swollen to an amazing degree and great damage was sustained: the waters rushed through the streets of St Thomas with great rapidity carrying everything before them, several bridges were thrown down and we are fearful of hearing still greater mischief done in other parts.

1800 A prodigious flood, such as the oldest person living had never before witnessed, occurred at Exeter and generally throughout the Kingdom. All the streets of St Thomas were inundated, the water reaching up to the windows and these poorer class inhabitants were in great distress.

1810 The river reached a very great height and washed away the remaining arches of Cowley Bridge. The whole of St Thomas and Exe Island were inundated. The devastation was "shocking and dismal in the extreme". Three vessels of large burthen were thrown completely on to the Quay and in the road leading from Okehampton Street the water was six feet deep.

1894 During the early hours of Monday morning the 13th November, following a prolonged storm of rain and hail, Cowick Street, Alphington Street, Exe Street, Tudor Street and Frog Street were all flooded to various depths.

1917 Exwick and the Exe Bridge area inundated by flood waters.

1920 More heavy flooding at Exwick and the low-lying area around Exe Bridge.

1929 Grievous flooding, in St Thomas and the Exe Bridge area.

1950 Significant flooding occurred at Exwick, Cowick Street and the Exe Bridge area.

1952 Serious floods at Exwick and the area to the west of Exe Bridge.

1960 Excessive rainfall in October and again in December led to 1,000 and 1,200 properties (respectively) being flooded in low-lying parts of Exeter. Peak discharge: 700 cumecs.

1978 River rose dramatically (400 cumecs) but Exeter Flood Defence Scheme successful in preventing flooding in low-lying parts of Exeter.

2000 October. Peak discharge of 500 cumecs, almost 40 years to the day from 1960 floods. Some flooding in unprotected area downstream of scheme - otherwise okay.